le Shuttle

EURO TUNNEL

I-SPY

THE CHANNEL TUNNEL

This book belongs to:

KT-172-170

It couldn't be easier to get to the Channel Tunnel. In Britain you simply take exit 11a from the M20.
I-Spy for 5

Look out for the sign telling you how far ahead the toll plaza is.
I-Spy for 5

'Get in Lane'. The pictograms make it clear which lane should be used by lorries and other types of traffic.
I-Spy for 5

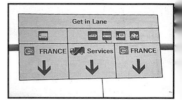

The same pictograms are used again but notice the green symbols show the lanes for lorries and cars going directly to Le Shuttle. And lorries should not enter the lane to service facilities for other traffic.
I-Spy for 5

This sign in France uses pictograms to direct you to eating areas, bureau de change, duty free shopping, information centre, and accommodation. For those aiming straight for Le Shuttle to Britain follow the sign for *Grande-Bretagne*.
I-Spy for 5

As well as the usual symbols, this is the main sign towards the toll system to take Le Shuttle to Britain. Notice lorries are directed on a separate route.
I-Spy for 5

All traffic more than 4.2 metres in height must take this route.
I-Spy for 5

The elegantly modernistic toll plaza. You can pay in cash (francs and sterling), and by cheque and debit and credit card.
I-Spy for 5

Sturdy concrete barriers with rubber bump strips and warning lights separate the lanes at the toll plaza.
I-Spy for 5

And notice the white reflectors for arrivals at night or in poor visibility. Every precaution has been taken to avoid difficulties.
I-Spy for 5

This lane is for motor cycles and right-hand drive cars with return tickets to present to the toll operator. It couldn't be clearer.
I-Spy for **5**

Here for right-hand drive cars, the return ticket can simply be inserted into an automatic machine . . .
I-Spy for **5**

. . . or left-hand drive cars. The planners seem to have thought of everything.
I-Spy for **5**

The Dynamic Lane is for Automatic Fare Collection. A regular user of the Tunnel may choose to buy a transmitter and fit it to the vehicle so that the fare can be debited automatically to the customer's account.
I-Spy for **10**

And this lane is for left-hand drive coaches and cars towing caravans that need to buy a ticket. Notice that emergency vehicles should also use this lane.
I-Spy for **5**

A stylish toll booth for Le Shuttle.
I-Spy for **5**

The digital displays at driver's-eye height give instructions on what to do. In this case 'Please Proceed'.
I-Spy for 5

This plain white cabinet contains the electronics for the Dynamic Lane.
I-Spy for 10

Here is the aerial that reads the sender on a vehicle passing through the Dynamic Lane.
I-Spy for 10

The automatic toll machines have slots for car- and coach-height drivers.
I-Spy for 5

The lights signal to go and the barrier rises to allow you through.
I-Spy for 5

5

Look out for the speakers for the public address system.
I-Spy for 5

To ensure that toll operators do not have to retain large amounts of cash, they can send it through these tubes to a central, secure depository . . .
I-Spy for 5

. . . and here it is.
I-Spy for 20

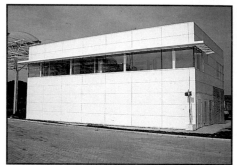

You're through the toll and on your way to *Grande-Bretagne* by Le Shuttle.
I-Spy for 5

But if you want to eat or drink, change money, or go to the duty free shopping, follow this sign to the Passenger Terminal Building.
I-Spy for 5

And, in Britain, turn right for France or left for the various amenities.
I-Spy for 5

There is not much choice at this roundabout – straight on for the car park or take the fifth exit to keep going for Le Shuttle.
I-Spy for 10

This sign shows the main facilities in the Passenger Terminal Building: eating; duty free; bureau de change; parking; toilets; and information.
I-Spy for 10

Heavy goods vehicles are directed to their own Amenity Building.
I-Spy for 15

Once again, it's straight on for Le Shuttle but there is parking either side for Heavy Goods Vehicles, and their drivers have their own service area; while another pictogram directs the lorries to . . .
I-Spy for 10

. . . the heavy goods vehicle inspection bay.
I-Spy for 10

Here is the sign showing the HGV service area, while parking for other vehicles is to the right, and coaches should proceed straight ahead.
I-Spy for 10

Parking for cars, disabled drivers, motor cycles, coaches, and cars towing caravans etc. straight ahead.
I-Spy for 5

This time cars towing caravans should turn right for their parking area.
I-Spy for 5

And disabled drivers turn right for their own parking area.
I-Spy for 5

How to find the two main parking areas with their rows and bays lettered and numbered . . .
I-Spy for 10

. . . like this. This is similar to the system used in airport car parks. Notice the speakers for the public address system.
I-Spy for 10

Once you have parked, pedestrians should follow the paths indicated . . .
I-Spy for 10

. . . and, to avoid accidents, pedestrians are warned to look out for traffic. You will see several signs like this one.
I-Spy for 5

Coach drivers are advised to set their passengers down in the area ahead.
I-Spy for 10

Coaches and caravans with on-board lavatory facilities may wish to empty them before joining Le Shuttle. This sign directs them to the special facilities provided . . .
I-Spy for 10

. . . for coaches. And don't forget to wash down the area afterwards . . .
I-Spy for 15

. . . with the special hose provided.
I-Spy for 15

Here's the sign showing where caravans should empty their chemical toilets . . .
I-Spy for 15

. . . and here is the facility with the tap from which water can be drawn to wash down the area afterwards.
I-Spy for 15

Here is the set-down and pick-up point for passengers on right-hand drive coaches . . .
I-Spy for 10

. . . and left-hand drive coaches.
I-Spy for 10

This way to the Passenger Terminal Building where there are shops, eating facilities, and so on.
I-Spy for 10

And here is the front of the Passenger Terminal Building at Calais with ample parking space. . .
I-Spy for 10

Look carefully and you will see these ball-shaped speakers, part of the public address system.
*I-Spy for **10***

. . . inside, look up to see the roof, cleverly designed for maximum strength and natural light.
*I-Spy for **10***

From a distance you can appreciate the highly innovative design of the Passenger Terminal Buildings at Folkestone.
*I-Spy for **10***

Its tent-like roof is made from a very tough artificial fabric and, through the glass panel in the cupola, laser displays may light up the night sky.
*I-Spy for **10***

Inside, overhead signs clearly indicate the facilities. In this case, toilets, a baby room, and telephones. And if you want to return to your car, go straight ahead.
I-Spy for **10**

Here are the women's toilets with disabled facilities and a baby room . . .
I-Spy for **10**

. . . similarly for men.
I-Spy for **10**

This sign is on the door of the men's shower room.
I-Spy for **10**

The door of the men's toilet is clearly marked with a pictogram so there are no language problems . . .
I-Spy for **10**

. . . as is the toilet for disabled travellers.
I-Spy for **10**

And this one is on the door of the baby room.
I-Spy for **10**

The wash room has been designed to be elegant, durable, and easy to keep clean.
I-Spy for 10

If you need to find a telephone, here is the pictogram to look for.
I-Spy for 10

The running person icon clearly directs you to an emergency exit.
I-Spy for 10

And here is an emergency phone in its bright-yellow box.
I-Spy for 10

In the rare event of an emergency, an alarm sounder like this one will be set off.
I-Spy for 15

Safety has been a main consideration throughout the whole Channel Tunnel system. In the Passenger Terminal Building look out for smoke detectors and automatic sprinklers.
I-Spy for 10

The louvre windows just beneath the cupola are operated by electric motors.
I-Spy for 10

On a mezzanine floor around the Passenger Terminal are administrative offices.
I-Spy for 10

And here is the elegant and stylish 'skylon' supporting the roof.
I-Spy for 10

This is the usual type of green sign indicating where the fire exit is.
I-Spy for 10

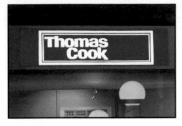

Inside the Passenger Terminal Building, you will find shops and facilities including a Thomas Cook bureau de change at both terminals . . .
I-Spy for 10

. . . in France, Relais H offers newspapers, books, and so on . . .
I-Spy for 10

. . . while McDonald's can provide a 'Big Mac' and more on both sides of the Channel.
I-Spy for 10

Two major motoring organizations are represented at Folkestone . . .

AA
I-Spy for 10

RAC
I-Spy for 10

16

And so is Hamleys, the famous toy emporium.
*I-Spy for **10***

W H Smith sells newspapers, books, and more at Folkestone.
*I-Spy for **10***

And here, too, Tie Rack, well known in high streets and at railway stations in Britain, also finds a place.
*I-Spy for **10***

For pharmaceutical and other products, you can call into Boots.
*I-Spy for **10***

And here is a typical family eating area.
*I-Spy for **10***

You may wonder why some areas are tarmacked while others are paved. You could probably work it out but the paved parts always mark some special area where you are required to stop, such as the toll plaza, frontier controls, etc.
I-Spy for 10

There are plenty of emergency phones outside the Passenger Terminal Building too.
I-Spy for 10

Throughout both Terminals, there is a maximum speed limit and no overtaking is permitted.
I-Spy for 10

All around the Terminal, look out for clocks. Remember that, once you have passed through the second frontier control, the time changes from British to French – Eurotunnel operates on French time. This clock has an analogue face, while on the platform they are digital.
I-Spy for 5

Fire hydrant signs are the same at the Folkestone Terminal as in the rest of Britain.
I-Spy for 10

The SV indicates the location of a water shut-off or stop valve while the AV marks an area valve which can control the water for a large area.
I-Spy for 10

While, in France, fire hydrants look like this.
I-Spy for 10

Look out for these closed-circuit television cameras . . .
I-Spy for 10

. . . and a battery of speakers for the public address system.
I-Spy for 10

Le Shuttle operates its own road vehicles in stylish livery.
A minibus . . .
I-Spy for 10

. . . and a saloon car.
I-Spy for 10

Having left the Passenger Terminal Building, turn left for Le Shuttle to France.
I-Spy for 10

Approaching the frontier controls at Calais, go through the green channel if you have nothing to declare.
I-Spy for 5

Notice the yellow lights.
I-Spy for 5

This lane is for cars, and cars with caravans, that come from countries outside the European Union
I-Spy for 5

This lane is for European Union cars and motor cycles with nothing to declare.
I-Spy for 5

At Folkestone, here is the UK frontier control.
I-Spy for 5

Coaches may be diverted to this special screened area . . .
I-Spy for 5

. . . passengers are then asked to leave the coach with their luggage and assemble in a waiting room while the coach may be thoroughly inspected.
I-Spy for 10

And here is the French frontier control on the Folkestone Terminal. Remember, that once you have passed through here, you are officially on French soil. Both sets of national controls are cleared on the departure terminal.
I-Spy for 5

Meanwhile, at Calais, here is an inspection pit which security officials can use when they inspect the undersides of vehicles.
I-Spy for 15

Here is a pedestrian sign in the frontier controls area.
I-Spy for 25

Where wordless pictograms are not used, all signs in and around the Terminal are in two languages. 'Stay in lane' . . .
I-Spy for 5

. . . and 'No Entry Except with Authority'
I-Spy for 15

Look out for these electronic vehicle height detectors.
I-Spy for 10

Cars under 1.85 metres in height use the two left-hand lanes; 1.85 metres and over, the right-hand lane.
I-Spy for 5

In France, overhead barriers are used to make sure that only vehicles under 1.85 metres high can proceed in this lane. The first is linked by chains and has a rubber strip at the bottom . . .
I-Spy for 5

. . . the second is a more substantial suspended boom . . .
I-Spy for 5

. . . and a vehicle 1.85 metres and over could not pass beneath this one without causing damage . . .
I-Spy for 5

. . . so if the vehicle you are travelling in is too high, you must now follow this sign.
I-Spy for 10

And all high vehicles follow this route . . .
I-Spy for 5

High vehicles
Véhicules hauts

Low vehicles
Véhicules bas

. . . while ordinary cars and motor cycles proceed in this direction.
I-Spy for 5

Le Shuttle: Access from the UK

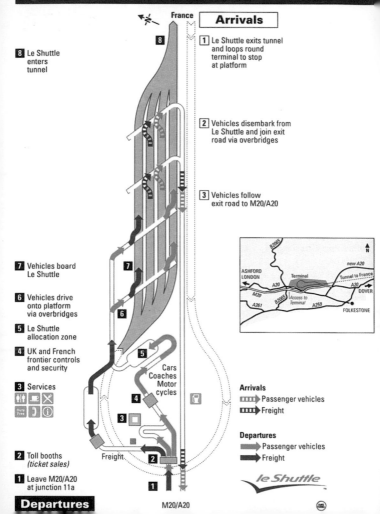

France

Arrivals

1 Le Shuttle exits tunnel and loops round terminal to stop at platform

2 Vehicles disembark from Le Shuttle and join exit road via overbridges

3 Vehicles follow exit road to M20/A20

8 Le Shuttle enters tunnel

7 Vehicles board Le Shuttle

6 Vehicles drive onto platform via overbridges

5 Le Shuttle allocation zone

4 UK and French frontier controls and security

3 Services

2 Toll booths *(ticket sales)*

1 Leave M20/A20 at junction 11a

Departures

Cars Coaches Motor cycles

Freight

Freight

M20/A20

Arrivals
▭▭▭▭ Passenger vehicles
▭▭▭▭ Freight

Departures
➤ Passenger vehicles
➤ Freight

le Shuttle

Inset map:
B2065 ASHFORD LONDON — new A20 — Terminal — Tunnel to France — A20 DOVER — M20 — A20 — A261 — B2065 — Access to Terminal — A259 — FOLKESTONE — N

Le Shuttle: Access from France

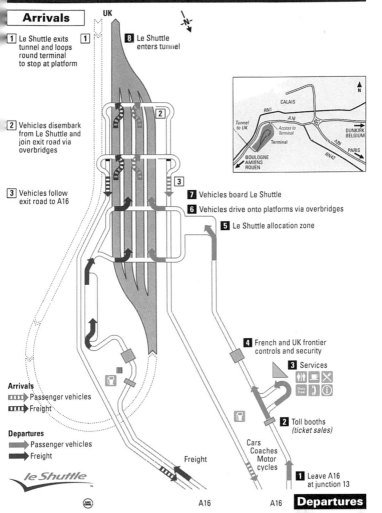

Arrivals

1 Le Shuttle exits tunnel and loops round terminal to stop at platform

2 Vehicles disembark from Le Shuttle and join exit road via overbridges

3 Vehicles follow exit road to A16

UK

N

8 Le Shuttle enters tunnel

7 Vehicles board Le Shuttle

6 Vehicles drive onto platforms via overbridges

5 Le Shuttle allocation zone

4 French and UK frontier controls and security

3 Services

Duty Free

2 Toll booths *(ticket sales)*

Cars
Coaches
Motor
cycles

1 Leave A16 at junction 13

Arrivals

▭▭▭ Passenger vehicles
▭▭▭▶ Freight

Departures

▬▬▶ Passenger vehicles
▬▬▶ Freight

Freight

le Shuttle ™

A16

A16

Departures

Inset map:
CALAIS
RN1
A16
Tunnel to UK
Access to Terminal
Terminal
BOULOGNE AMIENS ROUEN
RN43
DUNKIRK BELGIUM
A26 PARIS
N

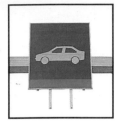

Now vehicles under 1.85 metres are separated again, into cars . . .
I-Spy for **5**

. . . motor cycles . . .
I-Spy for **5**

. . . and vehicles with disabled drivers.
I-Spy for **5**

This lane is for vehicles over 1.85 metres high, for those towing caravans and trailers, and for coaches.
I-Spy for **5**

And this lane for vehicles towing caravans.
I-Spy for **5**

Coaches use this lane.
I-Spy for **5**

Almost there! Here are the allocation lanes before you get to the loading ramp and platform.
I-Spy for **5**

Notice the lights at the start of each lane to indicate which one is in use.
I-Spy for **5**

And the lanes are separated by small concrete barriers . . .
I-Spy for **5**

. . . and white chevrons.
I-Spy for **5**

Even at this late stage, facilities have not been forgotten. Here is a toilet block.
I-Spy for **5**

This digital sign tells you which number lane you should use.
I-Spy for **5**

27

And here's ramp 10; this time the signal indicates no access.
I-Spy for 5

Down the ramp to the platform. Look out for the digital clock at the bottom . . .
I-Spy for 5

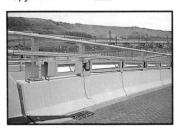

. . . and the special lighting all the way down.
I-Spy for 5

On reaching the platform, Le Shuttle staff direct you towards a loading carriage. Each passenger-vehicle shuttle will carry up to 120 cars and twelve coaches.
I-Spy for 5

You simply drive straight on to Le Shuttle . . .
I-Spy for 5

. . . . and you may drive up the ramp in the double-deck loading wagon. It takes about eight minutes to load a complete shuttle.
I-Spy for **5**

You continue to drive forward until you reach your carriage where staff tell you to stop. Then you can stay with your car, listen to Le Shuttle Radio, or stretch your legs. Perhaps it's a good time to plan the rest of your journey the other side.
I-Spy for **5**

Inside the carriage, every precaution has been taken to ensure your comfort and safety. Look out for the central gutter to carry any fuel leaking from cars to safety; the fire detection systems; and the two automatic systems (foam and halon gas) for dealing with fires. There is also a rising barrier at the end of each carriage to stop vehicles hitting the fire door.

The central gutter.
I-Spy for **5**

The fire detection systems.
I-Spy for **5**

The automatic fire extinguishing systems.
I-Spy for **5**

The rising barrier.
I-Spy for **5**

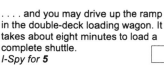

As well as the two automatic fire extinguishing systems, there are hand-held fire extinguishers in each carriage.
I-Spy for **5**

After the cars have been loaded, fire-proof doors close off each carriage. The double pass doors on each side of the central door allow access between carriages.
I-Spy for **5**

The carriages are sealed and pressurized and an air-conditioning system ensures the atmosphere is always clean and pleasant.
I-Spy for **5**

Notice the flexible bellows between carriages.

I-Spy for **5**

This alarm enables passengers to contact staff in an emergency
I-Spy for **5**

This doorway gives access to the stairs between the two decks in a double-deck carriage.
I-Spy for 5

Overhead displays provide on-board information.
I-Spy for 5

For every three double-deck carriages there are two toilets, one on each deck.
I-Spy for 5

One of the splendid shuttle locomotives. There is one loco at each end of the shuttle which may weigh up to 2600 tonnes and can travel at up to 140 km/h. Each loco can develop up to 7600 hp (5.6 MW).
I-Spy for 10

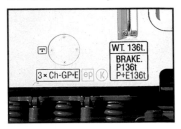

Like ordinary railway locomotives, Le Shuttle locos are numbered.
I-Spy for 15
Double for 9012, the first loco to bear Le Shuttle livery

The tare plate gives the weight of the locomotive.
I-Spy for 25

The driver sits on the left of the cab and, for safety, the door to the cab is double locked.
I-Spy for 15

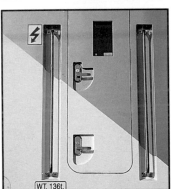

A pantograph on the shuttle loco-motive collects electricity from the overhead catenary carrying a supply at 25,000 volts.
I-Spy for 15

Here is a loading carriage for a single-deck shuttle that carries passenger vehicles 1.85 metres high and over. During loading, the bodywork telescopes to allow easy access for large vehicles.
I-Spy for 15

Here you can see how the flexible bellows between carriages appear from the outside.
I-Spy for 15

Look out for the ventilation ducts and the windows (for upper and lower decks).
I-Spy for 10

As you can see from the way this emergency door operates, the carriages are pressurized rather like the cabin of an aircraft.
I-Spy for 15

And as you can see from this plaque, building the locomotives involved multinational co-operation.
I-Spy for 15

The track is built to a standard gauge of 4 feet 8½ inches (1.43 metres) and outside the Tunnel uses conventional ballast. In the tunnels the continuously welded rails are set on rubber pads fixed to pairs of concrete blocks known as Sonneville Blocks. These are fitted with resilient pads and rubber boots cast into the concrete track bed. These concrete beams alongside the platform are used to support the shuttles while they are being loaded.

I-Spy for 25

These diesel-electric maintenance locomotives have been designed for use in the Tunnel.
I-Spy for 20

To prevent fumes from the diesel's exhaust polluting the Tunnel, the locomotive hauls a 'scrubber' to filter and clean up the exhaust.
I-Spy for 20

This maintenance vehicle has been designed to run both on rails and road.
I-Spy for 25

In the very unlikely event of a derailment in the Tunnel, special rerailing equipment has been designed. Nothing has been left to chance.
I-Spy for 25

This specially designed multipurpose vehicle has been nicknamed 'Thunderbird' because, like one of the vehicles in the television puppet series of that name, it can carry different pods to cope with different situations.
General maintenance . . .
I-Spy for 20

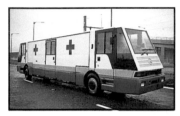

. . . medical emergency . . .
I-Spy for 20

. . . fire-fighting equipment.
I-Spy for 20

About thirty-five minutes after boarding is completed, you will start to unload on the other side of the Channel.
I-Spy for 5

You drive on to the unloading ramps.
I-Spy for 5

From the unloading ramps, the four lanes of traffic are reduced to three lanes, and then to two.
I-Spy for 5

In France, signs advise of the maximum speeds permitted (in km/h) in built-up areas, on ordinary roads, and on motorways.
I-Spy for 5

And here you are in France.
I-Spy for 10

It's good to feel welcome!
I-Spy for 10

On arrival, this sign tells you the region of France you are in.
I-Spy for 10

You can head for the motorway to Calais, Boulogne, etc.
I-Spy for 10

In Britain, the 'Drive on left' sign is in three principal European languages.
I-Spy for 10

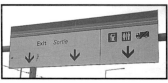

You are now about to leave the Channel Tunnel Terminal but, if necessary, drivers can refuel their cars and you can make use of the lavatories.
I-Spy for 10

Here's the exit road.
I-Spy for 10

The space-age architecture of the Customer Service Centre near the Folkestone Terminal.
I-Spy for 20

The *Siège* is the Central Administration building on the Terminal site in Calais.
I-Spy for 20

The Control Centre in Folkestone controls the whole Channel Tunnel railway system and all vehicle movement on the Folkestone Terminal.
I-Spy for 20

The Control Centre in Calais controls all vehicle movement on the Calais Terminal and also houses the back-up control system for the railway.
I-Spy for 20

Look out for the French Frontier Control administration building on the Folkestone Terminal.
I-Spy for 20

Seen from the old N1 in France, close to the Tunnel portal, here is the French electricity substation . . .
I-Spy for 20

. . . and on the Terminal site at Folkestone, here is the British electricity substation.
I-Spy for 25

To reduce the impact of high winds on the high-sided shuttle wagons, wind fences have been specially designed for both Terminals.
I-Spy for 10

And these small sections of wind fencing are along the centre of the platforms.
I-Spy for 5

Acoustic barriers reduce noise from the Folkestone Terminal. There are other fences, too. For example, as one of the defences against rabies, there is an animal-proof fence around the Tunnel portals in which the small-mesh fencing is 3 metres high above ground and sunk 40 centimetres into the ground.
I-Spy 5 for the acoustic barriers

In landscaping the two Channel Tunnel terminals, plans have included provision for the planting of about 100,000 trees and shrubs on the Folkestone Terminal and the same number of trees at the larger Calais site.
I-Spy for 5

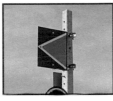

This very traditional pictogram warning of overhead high-tension electricity supply is in delightful contrast to the twenty-first-century technology of the project.
I-Spy for 25

The Terminal at Folkestone is the only place in Britain where you will see this trackside sign. The signalling for the Channel Tunnel system is known as TVM 430 and is similar to that used on SNCF's high-speed lines. TVM = track to train.
I-Spy for 20

In France, keep your eyes open for this warning sign: 'Danger of Death'.
I-Spy for 10

In an emergency, carriages from a shuttle emerging from the Tunnel can be isolated between these open-topped, protective walls.
I-Spy for 15

Extinguisher fluids are contained in tanks behind the protective walls and connect to these high-pressure nozzles above the walls.
I-Spy for 20

THE STORY OF FREIGHT

As you may have realized already, freight and passenger traffic follow different patterns through the system. Here is the sign in France indicating where to find the Freight Terminal. HGV vehicles carrying hazardous loads must follow the *Itinéraire obligatoire*.
I-Spy for **15**

The freight wagons must be able to carry HGVs of up to 44 tonnes although, on British roads, the maximum permitted weight is lower. Here is the way to a weighbridge in France.
I-Spy for **15**

Follow the sign for the freight shuttle. Once again, hazardous loads must keep to *Itinéraire obligatoire*.
I-Spy for **15**

In both French and English, this sign speaks for itself.
I-Spy for **15**

Here is the freight amenities building at Folkestone . . .
I-Spy for **10**

. . . and the frontier controls for HGVs.
I-Spy for **15**

For a closer inspection, HGVs may be directed into a security building like this one . . .
I-Spy for 10

. . . or like this one at Calais.
I-Spy for 15

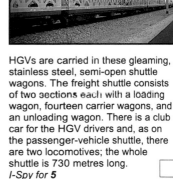

As in the case of passenger vehicles, once HGVs have passed the French frontier control at Folkestone, they are officially on French soil.
I-Spy for 10

HGVs are carried in these gleaming, stainless steel, semi-open shuttle wagons. The freight shuttle consists of two sections each with a loading wagon, fourteen carrier wagons, and an unloading wagon. There is a club car for the HGV drivers and, as on the passenger-vehicle shuttle, there are two locomotives; the whole shuttle is 730 metres long.
I-Spy for 5

In the centre of the shuttle there is one loading wagon and one unloading wagon. Here the loading plates are ready for use.
I-Spy for 15

Each shuttle wagon generally carries only one truck, . . .
I-Spy for 10

. . . each wagon is numbered, . . .
I-Spy for 15

. . . and lorry wheels are chocked to prevent movement.
I-Spy for 25

If the HGV is refrigerated, it can be plugged into one of these units inside the shuttle wagon, and the load will continue to be kept chilled or frozen.
I-Spy for 20

The clean lines of the HGV drivers' club car. Drivers may eat on board, and the time away from the lorry corresponds with one regulation rest period.
I-Spy for 10

High-speed Eurostar through-trains link London with Lille, Paris, and Brussels.
I-Spy
for 10 ☐

In Paris, the Eurostar trains run to and from the Gare du Nord.
I-Spy for 10 ☐

Look out for the specially built mezzanine where you can buy tickets and check in for the Eurostar service.
I-Spy for 10 ☐

Eurostar will operate from SNCF's (Société nationale des chemins de fer français) Lille Europe station. At Lille Flandres (left) a plaque (right) unveiled by President Mitterrand celebrates the opening of the TGV Nord Europe service.
I-Spy 10 for Lille Europe ☐
I-Spy 20 for Lille Flandres ☐

EUROSTAR

At Lille you can change to TGV services to different parts of France.
I-Spy for **10**

For the Eurostar service, there is an intermediate station at Calais Frethun.
I-Spy for **10**

In London, the Eurostar service operates out of Waterloo International Station . . .
I-Spy for **10**

. . . where you can buy your tickets . . .
I-Spy for **10**

. . . and look out for information displayed on overhead matrix signs.
I-Spy for **10**

Tunnelling work on the UK side was carried out from Shakespeare Cliff. Previous attempts also started from here, and you can see the hazardous path down the cliff that tunnellers used to reach the workings in the nineteenth century.
I Spy for **20**

Public access to the site is via a tunnel. The two portals to the left carry the railway line from Dover to Folkestone.
I-Spy for **20**

Much of the site at the base of Shakespeare Cliff has been reclaimed from the sea using the 4 million cubic metres of spoil from the excavation. Air temperature in the Tunnel is maintained by chilled water circulated through pipes pumped from cooling plants like this one at the foot of Shakespeare Cliff.
I-Spy for **20**

The reclaimed land is protected by these carefully designed wave walls.
I-Spy for **20**

In France, the Tunnel construction site was located at Sangatte just over 3 kilometres from the French Terminal at Calais. Spoil from the Tunnel was pumped as a slurry to a specially created reservoir at Fond Pignon.
I-Spy for 20

In France, the round portals of the two rail tunnels can be seen from the old N1 road. To the right, you can also see the service tunnel portal.
I-Spy for 20

In Britain, the tunnels emerge through an imposing rectangular portal although this is not easy to see.
I-Spy for 25